squish
SUPER AMOEBA

BY JENNIFER L. HOLM & MATTHEW HOLM

SCHOLASTIC INC.
New York Toronto London Auckland
Sydney Mexico City New Delhi Hong Kong

ISBN 978-0-545-39830-5

Copyright © 2011 by Jennifer Holm and Matthew Holm. All rights reserved. Published by Scholastic Inc., 557 Broadway, New York, NY 10012, by arrangement with Random House Children's Books, a division of Random House, Inc. SCHOLASTIC and associated logos are trademarks and/or registered trademarks of Scholastic Inc.

12 11 10 9 8 7 6 5 4 3 2 1   11 12 13 14 15 16/0

Printed in the U.S.A.   23

First Scholastic printing, September 2011

For Noreen!

AND MEG!!!!!! SHE'S SO CUTE!!!

too bad they're not amoebas.

EARTH.

OUR PLANET HOSTS A RICH DIVERSITY OF LIFE . . .

FROM LUSH RAIN FORESTS TO DRY DESERTS.

BUT BENEATH THIS WORLD LIES ANOTHER ONE.

8

A MICROSCOPIC WORLD.

THIS IS THE HOME OF THE **AMOEBA.**

AMOEBA

UH-MEE-BUH

BELONGS TO THE PROTISTA KINGDOM.

HAS NO BONES OR MOUTH OR EYES.

YOU NEED A MICROSCOPE TO SEE IT.

REPRODUCES BY SPLITTING.

YOU'LL BE TESTED ON THIS SOMEDAY, SO YOU'D BETTER BE PAYING ATTENTION.

A CREATURE MADE OF A SINGLE CELL.

SHALL WE TAKE A LOOK AT THE WORLD OF THIS SIMPLE BEING?

TWINKIE.

WHEN TROUBLE CALLS . . .

HELP!

AAAGH!!

AAAGH!!

NHO HAS THE COURAGE . . .

AAAHH!!!

TO DO WHAT'S RIGHT!

HEY, BIG, GREEN, AND SLIMY!

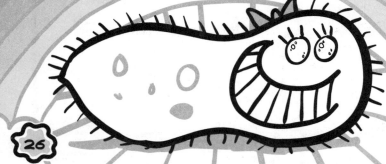

26

29

GRAB!

CRASH!

FLING!

WAAAHH!!!!

WAAAH!

MY BABY!

IS ALL LOST?

CLUNK

WAAAAHH!!!

SHIVER SHAKE

35

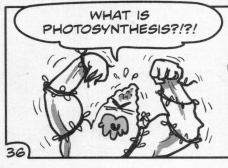

47

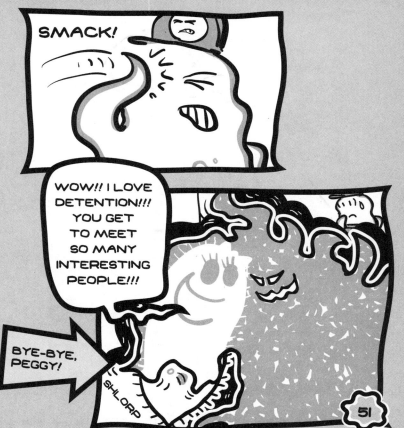

51

55

61

A FEW DAYS LATER.

RIIIIINN'NNGG!!!

Way to go, amoeba.

A moment, Squish.

HI, LYNWOOD!!! DO YOU WANT TO COME TO MY HOUSE AFTER SCHOOL AND SEE MY SLIME MOLD, FLUFFY?? HE'S SUPER CUTE!!!!

Love to. Will there be snacks?

YOU BET!!!!

Can't wait.

what'd i miss?

Lynwood's gonna eat Peggy after school.

I'M SO EXCITED!!!!

HE ALONE HAD THE COURAGE . . .

TO . . .

SPROING!!!

HI, LYNWOOD!!!! HOW ARE YOU??

Starving.

FROZEN IN FEAR.

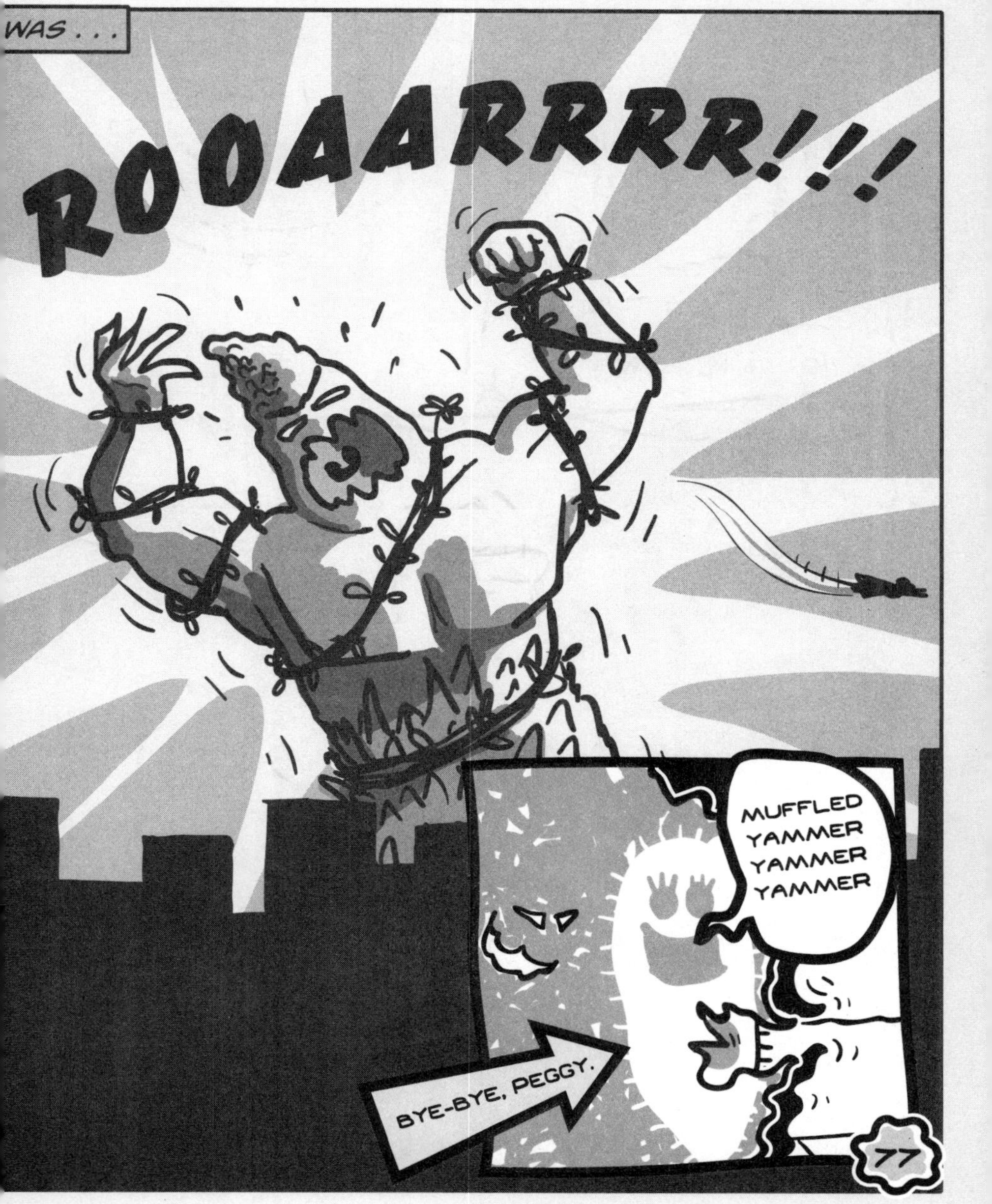
WAS . . .
ROOAARRRRR!!!
MUFFLED YAMMER YAMMER YAMMER
BYE-BYE, PEGGY.

79

89

FUN SCIENCE WITH POD!

hey, kids. want to grow mold?

it's easy. and fun.

get your supplies.

JAR

BREAD

WATER

YOU CAN DRAW SQUISH, TOO!!! HE'S SOOO CUTE!!!!!!

1.

2.

3.

4.

5.

6.

can i have your lunch money?

No!

Brother-and-sister team Matthew "Ink Boy" Holm and Jennifer "Writer Girl" Holm are longtime comic fans and the dynamic duo behind the award-winning **Babymouse** series. When not fighting the forces of evil, Jennifer writes novels, including the acclaimed **Turtle in Paradise** and two Newbery Honor winners, **Our Only May Amelia** and **Penny from Heaven**. Matthew is a graphic designer and freelance writer.